G000130184

METHOD FOR BASS
by
Julius Weissenborn

Revised by Fred Bettoney

TABLE OF CONTENTS

CARL FISCHER®
65 Bleecker Street, New York, NY 10012
http://www.carlfischer.com

ISBN 0-8258-0169-9

THE BASSOON

HISTORICAL SKETCH

The Bassoon (Italian—Il Fagotto, French—Le Basson, German—Der Fagott); a development of the crude eight-foot Bomhard or Pommer (Bass Pommer) was invented about 1539 by an Italian, Canon Afranio, of Ferrara. The most significant features of the invention were the doubling of the sounding tube on itself, and the introduction of a double reed to produce the tone in place of the original cup-shaped metal mouthpiece. The resulting instrument, called the "Dulciano", because of its mellowness of tone, had approximately the same shape as present-day Bassoons.

The compass and general arrangement of the original instruments are not known; but soon after the invention, instruments were constructed with eleven holes, on which the 7th, 9th, and 11th were operated by "clappers" or keys. This instrument had a possible scale, as follows:

PARTS OF THE BASSOON

The Bassoon consists of five parts: the S; the Wing, or Tenor Joint; the Boot; the Long Piece or Sounding Piece; and the Bell. It has a conical bore, practically throughout its entire length.

The S is a curved, delicate, metal tube and requires careful and constant care, as it has great influence on the formation and purity of tone produced. A poor or unsuitable S will play the best constructed Bassoon out of tune and spoil its tone. Just above the joint there is a small hole in the S, which when clogged, prevents some notes from sounding. To clean this hole, use a very small needle. To clean the S, run warm water through it, followed by a wire pipe cleaner. On account of the conical bore, use a cleaner that will go through the small end, as it would be extremely difficult to remove anything broken off inside.

During the first hundred and fifty years of its use, the Bassoon (or Dulciano, as it was called then) remained practically unchanged, which fact is exemplified by the use of the five-keyed Bassoon early in the Eighteenth Century. About this time, however, as the Bassoon came to have a fixed position as an orchestral instrument, the number of keys (there were then five, namely low Bb, D, Eb, E, and Ab) was increased, until, by the end of that century, instruments were made with ten keys. Furthermore, as greater demands were made of the players, they in turn demanded more of their instruments and the makers; and consequently the gradual development culminated in the modern Bassoon of nineteen to twenty-two keys.

In the past, Bassoons of various pitches were used, notably the Quart Bassoon, which was pitched a fourth higher than the ordinary Bassoon and the Quint Bassoon, pitched a fifth higher. Nothing definite is known of the origin of these types. At present these are not in common use; but the Contra-Bassoon, which is used only in grand orchestras, is a fitting bass to the woodwind section. This took the place of the Bass Ophiclide, which was unsatisfactory on account of its harsh, unpleasant tone. The range of the Contra-Bassoon is shown as follows:—

Parts for it are written the same as for the regular Bassoon but the actual sound is an octave lower.

Most Contra-Bassoons play as low as C, but it is possible to play to Bb by means of an extra joint.

The fingerings are essentially the same as for the regular Bassoon but the reed is considerably larger. The tone is smooth and powerful, although the lower notes can be played softer than on the regular Bassoon.

After the S, comes the Tenor Joint. This section, like the other sections of the Bassoon, is usually made of maple, because of the mellow, somewhat cloudy tone produced. Other woods are used, such as Rosewood and Palisander. On all modern Bassoons, the Tenor Joints are lined with rubber, to overcome the cracking of the wood, and to maintain accuracy of bore. After being used, the instrument should be dried out with a silk or wool swab. This operation, constantly repeated, as is necessary, would soon wear out anything but the hardest wood.

The Boot, next in order, and by far the most complicated part of the Bassoon, has two sound pipes in one piece of wood. These two pipes are joined at the bottom in various ways. Some manufacturers use a metal coupling; others, a cork device. The cork is easier to keep tight, and may be kept well greased. Metal couplings are likely to wear and leak. If the instrument leaks at any part, it will play with great difficulty.

The next part, the Long Piece, is a single tube on which are the Eb, D, Db, C and B♮ keys, all operated by the thumb of the left hand.

The next piece, the Bell, is also a single tube on which there is but one key, the Bb.

To put the Bassoon together, take the Tenor Joint and Long Piece and lay them together. This will bring the joints at the right position to be placed in the boot. Always place both joints in the boot at the same time. Otherwise, it is possible to twist a joint, and, if pushed in while out of line, the joint may crack. When both joints are entered, place the boot on the floor and push each joint in straight, as far as it will go. Then, take the bell and push it or in such a way that the keys are in line with each other. In putting on the S, hold it as near the joint as possible. Never try to change its position by pushing sideways near the reed end. If the joint is tight, it is very easy to twist the S, or even to break it off.

The joints are made tight in either of two ways: by winding with thread, or by fitting with sheet cork. Whichever way is used, always make the fit just tight enough to hold the joints together. If too loose, the instrument may fall apart; if too tight, the putting together and taking apart are rendered difficult.

In taking the Bassoon apart, first remove the S, then the Bell, then the Long Piece, and last the Tenor Joint. You will find that joints come apart much more easily when given a slight twist. To keep the joint tenons in good condition, an occasional application of joint grease is necessary.

THE REED

The reed, the actual vibration-producing medium, is a piece of cane of the same nature and quality as used on clarinet, saxophone and oboe reeds. This cane is cut from a well known rush which grows in almost all the still waters of Southern Europe. The Bassoon reed is double, being bent over on itself, shaped, and then wired and bound with string. The blade is cut away to a thinness most suitable for the production of the tone. The quality of the reed depends chiefly on the cane. The best workman cannot make a good reed from poor cane. With a good reed, the Bassoon will be in good tune and tone in every register, but the player must determine what is good for himself. There is no one size and shape of reed for everybody. Some require a large reed, some a small, some a strong reed, some a weak. So, each player must fit his reeds himself to get the best results. A reed, too short or too small, will be too high in pitch; and a reed too long and wide, will be flat.

FITTING THE REED

The following general rules will give an idea of how to start to fit reeds.

First of all, never try to play or work on a dry reed. A reed cannot be too wet; and if it is not wet enough, it is very likely to crack. It is necessary to have only the blade of the reed wet, and holding it in water up to the wire for a half minute is generally enough to accomplish this end.

The cutting or scraping away must be regular and smooth, with a slight taper to the end. If lumpy or irregular, a reed can not function properly. If too thick at the end, a "piano" attack is impossible. If the reed blows hard in every register, it is too thick all over; if the low notes alone do not come easily, the reed is too thick near the wire; if the high notes do

not come, the edges and tip are too thick. In working on a reed, always work backwards from the tip, taking more from the sides than in the centre. The strength and heart of the reed is in its ability to stay open. If it is cut or scraped away too much down the centre, it will collapse. There are three ways of taking cane off; filing, scraping, and cutting. Either way may be used successfully. In filing, a rather rough file is necessary, with sufficient water on the file to wash away the grindings. To scrape or cut, a very sharp knife is necessary.

In working on the blade, the danger of cracking will be lessened considerably by having a V shaped piece of wood or metal, called a "Tongue," to insert in the opening, to hold the cane up to the knife or file. This tongue should be tapered on all sides and only a little thicker than the opening of the reed at the wide end. The opening of the reed should not be too close together, or it will not be possible to produce a full tone, and the low notes will not sound. On the other hand, should the opening be too wide, it will be difficult to control the tone. The opening may be altered slightly by squeezing very carefully with the fingers or pincers on the wires.

If the reed "blows" fairly well in every register, but plays too low in pitch, make the reed a little narrower. This is best done with a file. If the reed "blows" easily or softly and plays flat, especially the open e and f, cut the end off a little. Cut off only a 32nd of an inch at a time. This is done best with sharp scissors. Be sure to have the reed wet and to press both sides together.

Very often a reed which does not "blow" very well at first, will, by mere use, improve considerably. It is not to be expected that every reed will be good; but, by patient work and practice, many reeds, which at first seem poor, can be made to give general satisfaction.

TONE AND GENERAL CHARACTERISTICS

There is no other instrument productive of so many different tone colors, and effects, as the Bassoon. Its position as the bass of the woodwinds is unquestioned; its sonorous, mellow tone in the low register makes it practically indispensable. Its beautiful tenor voice in its middle and upper registers, renders melodies with fine effect. It is peculiarly adapted to the playing of allegro passages, and has possibilities for humorous effects, especially when it jumps from one register to another. It has been called "the clown of the orchestra". However, some performers, who have no knowledge of its real possibilities when used properly, degrade it by producing disagreeable sounds.

In the works of Mozart and Beethoven and other great masters of the symphony, important parts are given to the Bassoon.

POSITION OF THE BODY WHILE
HOLDING THE INSTRUMENT

It is best to become accustomed to stand while practising. The reed should be at such an angle as not to necessitate bending or twisting the head in any way. Adjust the supporting cord or strap, and if necessary, bend the S slightly. Hold the head up well and the shoulders straight so that breathing is perfectly free. Place fingers 1, 2, and 3 of the left hand on the corresponding holes on the Tenor Joint and the right hand fingers on the holes in the Boot. If the instrument has a holder, simply place the right hand on it. If it has no holder the thumb of the right hand should rest on the instrument, when not on the hole. The Boot should rest against the right thigh. Hold the elbows in their natural position.

PRODUCING THE TONE

Place the reed firmly on the S, in a horizontal position. Do not slant the reed, as doing so makes it necessary to hold the head in an unnatural position. Lay the lips over the teeth and put the reed between the lips up to a point about 3-8 of an inch from the wire. Hold the reed firmly and draw the lips tightly over the teeth. The pressure required is determined by the note to be played, the low notes requiring practically no pressure. Pressure is increased as the scale ascends. When the reed is in position, the tongue should be able to touch the end of the reed. Blow and say "tu" or "du". Never start a tone by blowing from the chest, as one does in saying "hu". Always start by an attack with the tongue.

A chart showing fingering for every note is given on page 5. Where more than one fingering is given for a certain note, the first one is generally the one most commonly used. The others will be found very useful in certain passages and combinations of notes. Naturally there are many combinations and groups of fingering not to be found on the chart which the player will find in the progress of practice.

5479-3

THE GERMAN BASSOON

PARTS OF THE BASSOON

A The Bell
B The Wing *(Tenor Joint)*
C The Long Joint
D The Boot
E The Crook

Sound Holes

Left Hand The Wing
I
II
III

Right Hand [The Boot]
I
II
III

Keys

1 Contra Bb
2 B
3 C
4 D
5 High C or Binding Key
6 A
7 C♯ connected with D for trills
8 Bb
9 E
10 F♯ low
11 Ab
12 Ab
13 F
14 F♯ middle
15 Bb
16 C♯
17 C♯ low
18 Eb

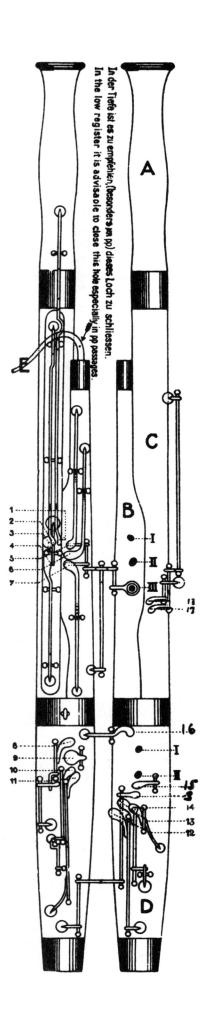

In der Tiefe ist es zu empfehlen, (besonders im pp) dieses Loch zu schliessen.
In the low register it is advisable to close this hole especially in pp passages.

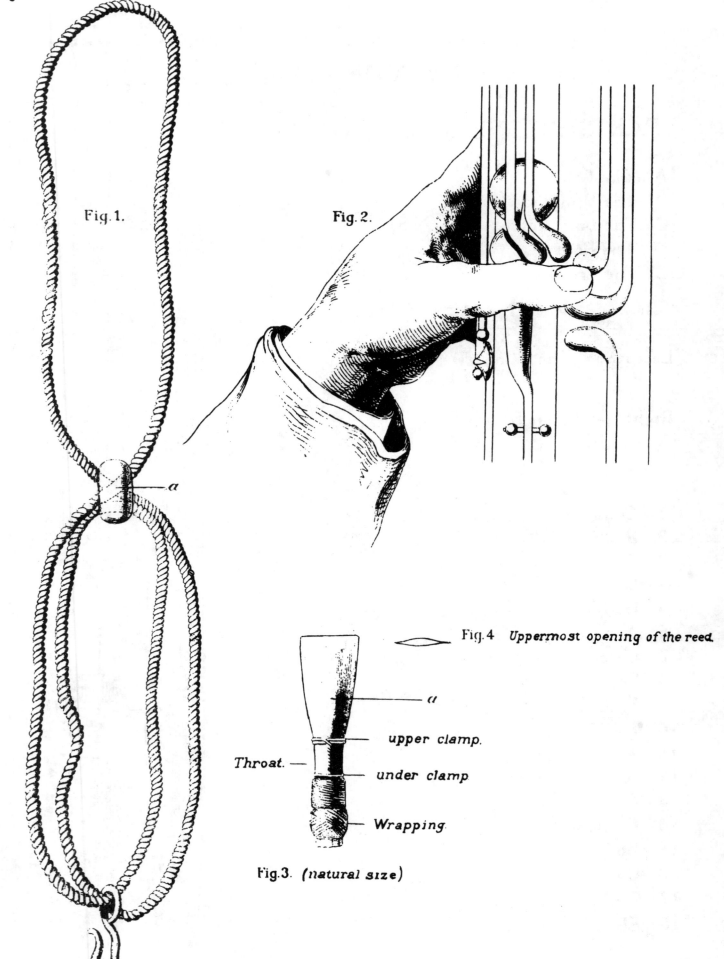

Fig. 1.

Fig. 2.

Fig. 4 *Uppermost opening of the reed.*

a

upper clamp.

Throat. —

under clamp.

Wrapping.

Fig. 3. *(natural size)*

5458-2

Studies on the Major Scales
In the keys most used.

These scales lie in the middle register of the Bassoon.   It is advisable to study the
sharp major scales before taking up minor scales.   These scales should be played daily.
Scales, major and minor, covering the entire range of the bassoon may be found farther
on in this book.

Models of Articulation.
To be applied to both major and minor scales.

Studies on the Minor (Melodic) Scales
In the keys most used.

Models of Articulation.

To be applied to both major and minor scales.

Praktische Uebungen.

Practical exercises.

Der Ton wird erzeugt durch den Zungenstoss „Da" oder „ta."

Das Heben und Fallenlassen der Finger muss namentlich bei Bindungen äusserst präcis geschehen. Hauptsächlich ist dies dann zu beobachten, wenn zwei und mehr Finger gleichzeitig zu heben oder fallen zu lassen sind.

The tone is produced by the tongue uttering „da" or „ta."

The rise and fall of the fingers especially where two notes are bound together, must be made with the greatest precision. — This is to be noticed particularly when two or more fingers are to rise or fall simultaneously.

I.

Ruhige Viertel. — **Die Töne ihrem vollen Werte nach aushalten!**
Quarter notes. — *The tones to be held their full time - value!*

Schüler.
Pupil.

Lehrer.
Teacher.

II.

Ruhige Viertel. – Die Töne richtig aushalten!
Quarter Rests. – The tones held properly!

Ruhige Viertel wie vorher. – *Quarter rests as before.*

Ruhige Achtel. - *Eighth notes.*

Allegretto.   **Larghetto.**

Ruhige Achtel. - *Eighth notes.*

Andante.

Sch.
P.

L.
T.

Staccato-

Der runde Punkt (·) bezeichnet das weiche, der spitze (ᵥ) das scharfe Staccato. Das leztere schreibt man sehr häufig auch folgendermassen:

Staccato=

The dot (·) designates the soft, the point (ᵥ) the sharp staccato. The latter is very frequently written in the following manner:

III.

Andante.

Andante.

14

IV.

Der Schüler muss nach und nach lernen, kurze Stücke in einem Athem zu blasen. So lange ihm dies noch nicht gelingt, ist, wenn Pausen fehlen, da zu athmen, wo der musikalische **Gedanke** einen Ruhepunkt hat oder wenigstens nicht zerrissen wird. Solche Stellen sind hier mit einem Komma bezeichnet.

The pupil should, little by little, learn to play short pieces, all in one breath. As long as this remains impossible to him he should take breath, when no pauses occur, at those places where the musical thought has a point of rest or at least will not be broken. Such places are indicated in this work, by a comma.

V.

16

L'istesso tempo.

Moderato.

Ausführung.- Executed.

Mässiges Walzertempo. - Moderate Walz-tempo.

Allegro moderato.

Meno allegro.

Più lento.

VI.

18

Der Ton „B" ist bei den nächsten Uebungen mit der Daumenklappe zu greifen.

In the following exercises the note Bb is to be played with the thumb-valve.

VII.

20

Patetico.
(Scharf accentuirt.) - (Sharply accented.)

VIII.

Moderato.

Ruhig. - Quietly.
Eins. zwei. drei. vier.
One, two, three, four,

5463-63

22

Das Portamento, welches man mit Punkten und Bogen (⌣ ....) bezeichnet, ist ein getragenes, mehr dem Legato ähnliches Staccato. Bei dieser Vortragsweise sind die einzelnen Töne sehr weich anzugeben, aber nicht wie beim Staccato kurz abzustossen.

The portamento, which is indicated by points and ties: (⌣ ....) is a sustained, legato-like staccato. In rendering this, the single tones are to be played very softly but not broken off shortly as in staccato.

IX.

X.

24

Marcia funebre.

XI.

Andante con moto.

Allegro moderato.

Allegro non tanto.

Mit vollem Ton. – *With full tone.*

Andante con moto.

dolce

Allegro vivace.

L'istesso tempo.

Andante.

Mit vollem Ton. – *With full tone.*

Moderato.

XII

28

29

5463 63

XIII.

In den Bindungen  öffnet man kurz die Schleifklappe.

To the these open the binding-valves for a brief space.

XIV.

Moderato. Bdur-Tonleiter.) – (B♭ major scale.)

Andante.

Moderato assai. (Bmoll-Tonleiter.) – (B♭ minor scale.)

XV.

Lento.

Moderato.

Andantino.

34

XVI.

36

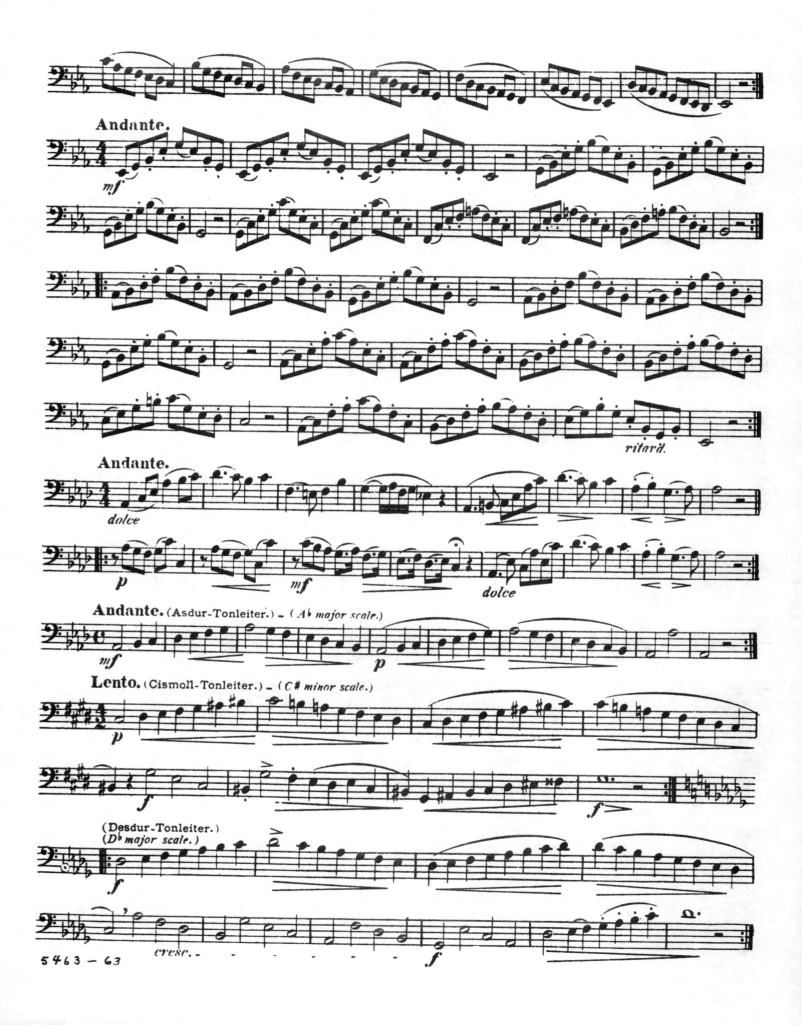

XVII.

Risoluto.
Mit vollem Ton. — *With full tone.*

(Cdur-Tonleiter durch 2 Octaven.) — *(C major scale through 2 Octaves.)*

Andante.

Andante.

L'istesso tempo.

(Octaven.) — *(Octaves.)*

Moderato.
(Terzen.) – (*Thirds.*)

Moderato.
(Quarten.) – (*Fourths.*)

Andante.
(Quinten.) – (*Fifths.*)

XVIII.

Poco allegro.

dolce

espress.

poco forte

poco forte

Moderato.

Moderato.

poco forte

(Dmoll - Tonleiter durch 2 Octaven.) - (Dminor scale through 2 Octaves.)

5463-63

40

Moderato assai.

L'istesso tempo.　　　　　L'istesso tempo.

Moderato assai.

(Ddur-Tonleiter durch 2 Octaven.) - (Dmajor scale through 2 Octaves.)

Allegretto.

TRIO.

(Hmoll-Tonleiter durch 2 Octaven.) - (Bminor scale through 2 Octaves.)

Andante.

D.C. al Fine.

5463-63

XIX.

L'istesso tempo.

g.

L'istesso tempo.

h.

i. (Bmoll - Tonleiter durch 2 Octaven.) – (*B♭ minor scale through 2 Octaves.*)

sonoro

k. **Moderato.**

5463-63

XX.

44

Langsam.

Allegro ma non troppo.

(Emoll - Tonleiter durch 2 Octaven.) _ (Eminor scale through 2 Octaves.)

Allegro.

Mit vollem Ton.
With full tone.

(Fdur-Tonleiter durch 2 Octaven.) _ (Fmajor scale through 2 Octaves.)

XXI.

46

Allegro.

(Gmoll-Tonleiter durch 2 Octaven.)
(G minor scale through 2 Octaves.)

Mit vollem Ton.—With full tone.

Marcia.
risoluto

poco forte

(Esdur-Tonleiter durch 2 Octaven.) - (Eb major scale through 2 Octaves.)

Mit vollem Ton.—With full tone.

8463-63

XXII.

(Asdur-Tonleiter durch 2 Octaven.) - (A♭ major scale through 2 Octaves.)

Mit vol'em Ton. - *With full tone.*

Langsam. - *Slowly.*
poco forte

Ruhiges Zeitmass. - *Quiet tempo.*
p

Moderato.
Mit vollem Ton. - *With full tone.*

Moderato.
mf

XXIII.

Langsam. (Amoll-Tonleiter durch 2 Octaven.) — (*A minor scale through 2 Octaves.*)
Slowly.

Mit vollem Ton.
With full tone.

Allegro moderato.

dolce

5463--63

Langsam. (Adur-Tonleiter durch 2 Octaven.) — (A major scale through 2 Octaves.)
Slowly.

Mit vollem Ton.
With full tone.

Andante con moto.

Langsam. (Fismoll-Tonleiter durch 2 Octaven.) — (F# minor scale through 2 Octaves.)
Slowly.

Mit vollem Ton. — With full tone.

Langsam. — Slowly.

Langsam. (Edur-Tonleiter durch 2 Octaven.) — (E major scale through 2 Octaves.)
Slowly.

Mit vollem Ton. — With full tone.

Allegro giusto.

Ausführung:
Executed:

p

cresc.

f   *f*

f

p

f

fp

Langsam. (Cismoll-Tonleiter durch 2 Octaven.) – (*C# minor scale through 2 Octaves.*)
Slowly.

Mit vollem Ton. – *With full tone.*

Andante con moto.

mf espress.

fz

Fine. *p dolce*

D.C. al fine.

XXIV.

Langsam. - *Slowly.*
(Hdur-Tonleiter durch 2 Octaven.) – (*B major scale through 2 Octaves.*)
Mit vollem Ton. – *With full tone.*

Larghetto.

Langsam. (Gismoll-Tonleiter durch 2 Octaven.) – (*G♯ minor scale through 2 Octaves.*)
Slowly.

Mit vollem Ton. – *With full tone.*

Allegretto.

Langsam. - *Slowly.*
(Fisdur-Tonleiter durch 2 Octaven.) – (*F♯ major scale through 2 Octaves.*)

Mit vollem Ton. *With full tone.*
(Gesdur-Tonleiter durch 2 Octaven.) – (*G♭ major scale through 2 Octaves.*)

Allegretto.

5463-63

Allegretto.

Langsam. - Slowly.
(Esmoll-Tonleiter durch 2 Octaven.) - (E♭ minor scale through 2 Octaves.)

Mit vollem Ton. - With full tone.

(Dismoll-Tonleiter durch 2 Octaven.) - (D♯ minor scale through 2 Octaves.)

Commodo.

Maestoso.

5463-63

XXV.

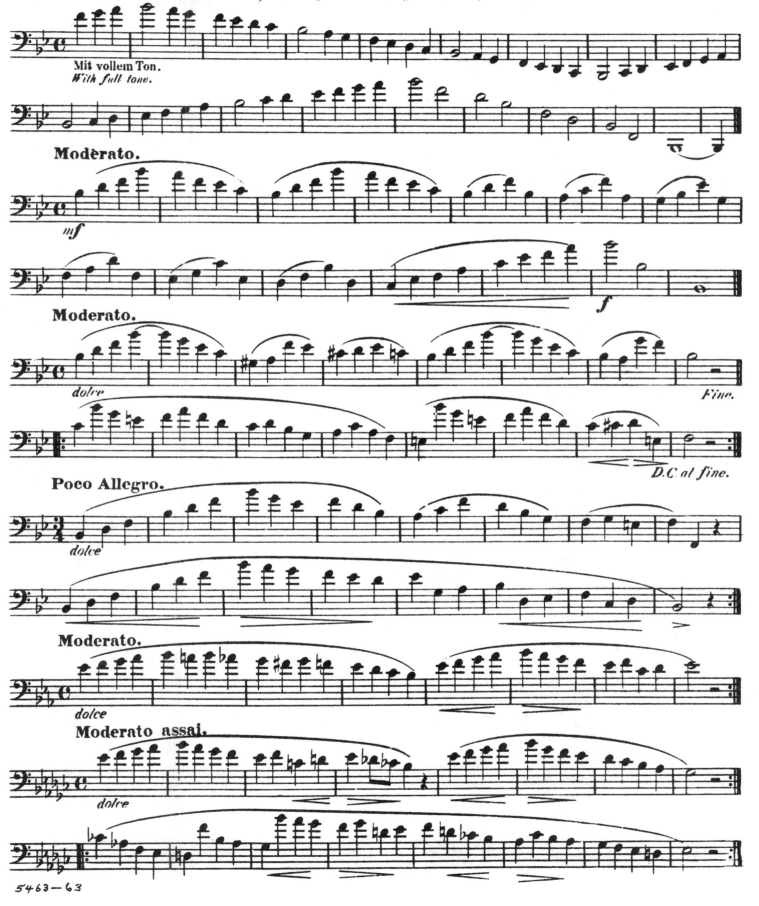

Der Tenorschlüssel. | The tenor-clef.

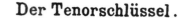

Andante sostenuto.

Andante con moto.

Sehr häufig werden die Töne der ein - und zweige-strichenen, sowie die der kleinen Octave, mitunter auch noch tiefere, für Fagott im **Tenorschlüssel** geschrieben. Es ist darum eine sehr wichtige Aufgabe für den Schüler, sich mit diesem Schlüssel vollkommen vertraut zu machen. Wie viel praktischer und beque-mer das Schreiben und Lesen der hohen Töne im Tenor-schlüssel als im Bassschlüssel ist, zeigen die letzten Uebungen, welche in beiden Schlüsseln notirt wurden. Zur Erlernung des Tenorschlüssels benutze man fol-gende kleine Tabelle:

Very frequently the tones of the one- or two-lined as well as the little octave, including too still lower ones, are written for the Bassoon, in the tenor-clef. It is therefore a very important lesson for the pupil, to make himself thoroughly familiar with this clef. How much more practical and com-fortable it is to read and write the high tones, in the tenor instead of the Bass-clef is shown by the last exercises written out in both clefs. To learn the tenor-clef use the following table:

Die Verzierungen.

Verzierungen (Ornamente) nennt man die zur Ausschmückung melodischer Hauptnoten eingeschobenen Nebentöne von geringem Zeitwerthe, welche gewöhnlich durch besondere Zeichen oder kleinere Noten angedeutet sind. Vielfach werden auch solche Verzierungen, deren Ausführung bei der gewöhnlichen Schreibweise eine verschiedenartige sein kann, vom Componisten in bestimmten Notenwerthen ausgeschrieben. Von den vielen früher üblichen Verzierungen sind nur noch folgende im Gebrauch: der **Vorschlag**, der **Nachschlag**, der **Pralltriller**, der **Mordent**, der **Doppelschlag** und der **Triller**.

Der **Vorschlag** wird mit kleinen Noten geschrieben, welche bei der Takteintheilung nicht in Anrechnung kommen. Man unterscheidet folgende Arten desselben: den **langen, accentuirten** und den **kurzen, accentlosen** Vorschlag. Bei der ersten Art wird die Vorschlagsnote mit dem ihr zukommenden Werthe aufgezeichnet, welcher dann bei der Ausführung von dem der folgenden Hauptnote abzuziehen ist. Z. B.

The embellishments.

The little notes of small time value which are used to adorn the principal notes of a melody are called embellishments or ornaments and are usually indicated by especial signs or by small notes. Many times those embellishments whose execution may be different from that of the common notation are written out by the composer just as they are to be played. Of the earlier embellishments the following, only, are still in use: The grace note, the turn, the short trill, the Mordent, the double grace note and the Trill.

The grace note is written in small notes and is not reckoned in the time. One must distinguish the different kinds of grace notes: the long, accented, and the short, unaccented grace note. — The first mentioned is given its real time value which is to be afterwards deducted from the value of the principal note following it. e.g.:

Die andere Art unterscheidet sich von der ersten dadurch, dass die Vorschlagsnote einen Querstrich durch die Fahne (den Achtel- oder Sechzehntelhaken) hat:

The other grace-note is distinguished from the first in that its stem has a stroke through it

Der **Nachschlag** wird wie der Vorschlag mit kleinen Noten notirt, welche von der vorhergehenden Hauptnote abzuziehen sind. Z. B.

The turn is written like the grace-note in small notes whose time value is to be deducted from the immediately preceding principal note. e.g.

Für gewöhnlich braucht man den Nachschlag zum Abschluss eines Trillers.

The turn is generally used to close a trill.

Der **Pralltriller** wird mit ᴧᴧ bezeichnet und durch einmaligen raschen Wechsel der Hauptnote mit der oberen Secunde hervorgebracht. Soll die Hilfsnote chromatisch verändert werden, so steht über dem Zeichen ein ♯, ♭ oder ♮:

The short-trill is indicated by ᴧᴧ and is executed by a single quick exchange of the principal note with its upper second. If the auxiliary note is to be changed chromatically the sign of transposition ♯, ♭ or ♮ is placed over the sign. e.g.:

Der **Mordent** wird mit ⬿ bezeichnet; er unterscheidet sich vom Pralltriller nur dadurch, dass die Hauptnote nicht mit der oberen, sondern mit der unteren kleinen Secunde abwechselt.

The Mordent is indicated by ⬿; it is different from the short-trill (Prall-triller) in that the principal note is not exchanged with the upper, but with the semitone below it.

Der **Doppelschlag**, welcher mit ∞ bezeichnet wird, ist aus 2 Vor- oder Nachschlägen, einem von oben und einem von unten, zusammengesetzt. Seine rhytmische Ausführung ist je nach der Taktart und dem Tempo des Musikstücks verschieden. Soll in den Nebentönen eine chromatische Veränderung eintreten, so stehen wie beim Pralltriller und Mordent über oder unter dem ∞ kleine Versetzungszeichen:

The double grace-note which is designated by ∞ is the combination of two grace notes or turns. Its rhythmical execution always depends upon the measure and the tempo of the composition. If a chromatic alteration be made in the changing notes, a ♯, ♭ or ♮ should be placed over or under the sign as in the short-trill and the mordent.

8. Vivace.

9. Allegro vivace.

10. Appassionato.

Der **umgekehrte Doppelschlag** (siehe Bsp. 10) kommt in neuerer Zeit sehr oft in Anwendung, doch wird derselbe gewöhnlich in Noten ausgeschrieben, und ist die ursprüngliche Bezeichnung, das gewöhnliche Zeichen umgekehrt oder aufrecht stehend: ∾ oder S, fast ganz ausser Gebrauch gekommen.

Der **Triller** — in der Notenschrift mit *tr* oder *tr⌇* bezeichnet — besteht aus einem schnellen und gleichmässigen, den Werth der vorgeschriebenen Note ausfüllenden Wechsel des Hauptontones mit der nächsten, je nach der Tonart, einen halben oder ganzen Ton höheren Tonstufe. Der Triller beginnt immer mit der Hauptnote: , so: , wenn nicht vor derselben eine oder mehrere kleine Noten stehen, durch welche ein anderer Anfang vorgeschrieben ist. Z. B.

The inverted double grace note (*See ex: 10*) *is used very often in our day, but is generally written out, the original sign (the ∾ inverted or S) is almost obsolete.*

The trill, indicated in the notation in this manner: tr or tr⌇ is a quick and even changing of the principal note with the next one, having the time value of the note it embellishes and is a whole or half tone higher, according to the key in which it is written. The trill always begins with the principal note so: *if there be no small notes written out in which a different beginning is indicated. For example.*

Ausführung: – Executed:

Einen längeren Triller lässt man langsam beginnen und ganz allmälig schneller werden.

A long trill is begun slowly and gradually accelerated.

Zum Abschluss eines längeren Trillers ist stets ein **Nachschlag** erforderlich. Bei neueren Musikstücken sind selbige in der Regel (wie bei a) mit kleinen Noten angegeben, während sie bei älteren gewöhnlich fehlen.

At the end of a long trill a turn is always used. In modern compositions this is, as a rule, written out as at (a) while in the older compositions it is usually wanting.

a)

Ausführung:
Executed:

XXVI.

Der lange Vórschlag. – *The long grace note.*
Andante sostenuto.

Der kurze Vorschlag. – *The short grace note.*
Allegretto.

Der mehrnotige Vorschlag. – *The grace note of several notes.*
Ausführ. Patetico.
Executed:

Andante maestoso.

Ausführ.
Executed:

Der Nachschlag. – *The turn.*
Polonaise.

Der Pralltriller. – *The short trill.*
Allegretto e con grazia.

Der Mordent. – *The Mordent.*
Allegro.

Der Doppelschlag. - *The double grace note.*
Andante.

Der umgekehrte Doppelschlag.- *The inverted double grace note.*
Andante sostenuto.

Der Triller.- *The trill.*
Allegretto moderato.

5463-63

ANHANG.

Tägliche Studien.

Diese Studien sind zur Entwickelung der Fertigkeit je nach Bedürfniss nach und nach vorzunehmen.

Einfache und variirte diatonische Tonleitern.

a. In Dur.

SUPPLEMENT.

Daily studies.

These studies are to be practised, as required, to develope the technic by degrees.

Simple and varied diatonic scales.

a. In major.

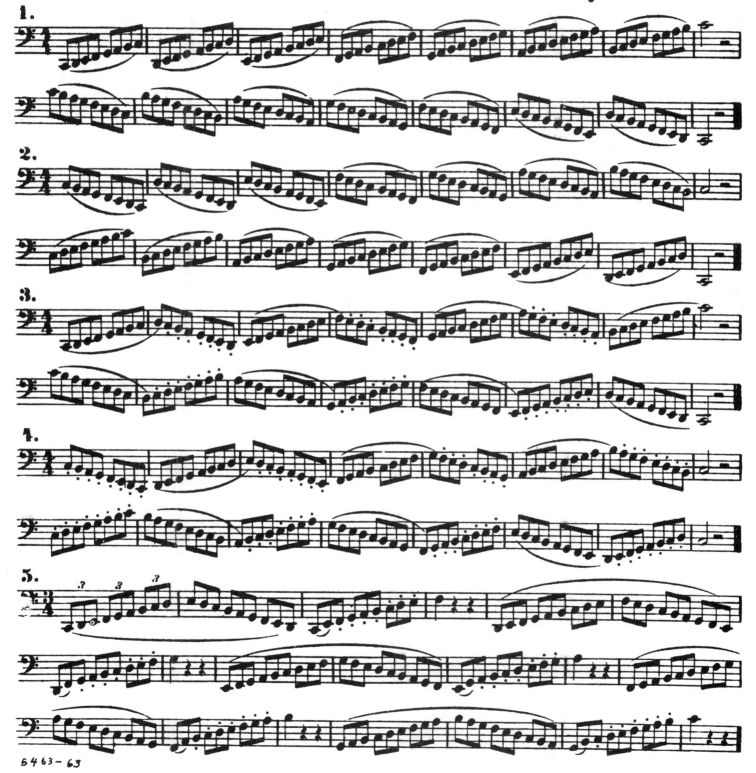

5463-63

b. In Moll.   b. In minor.

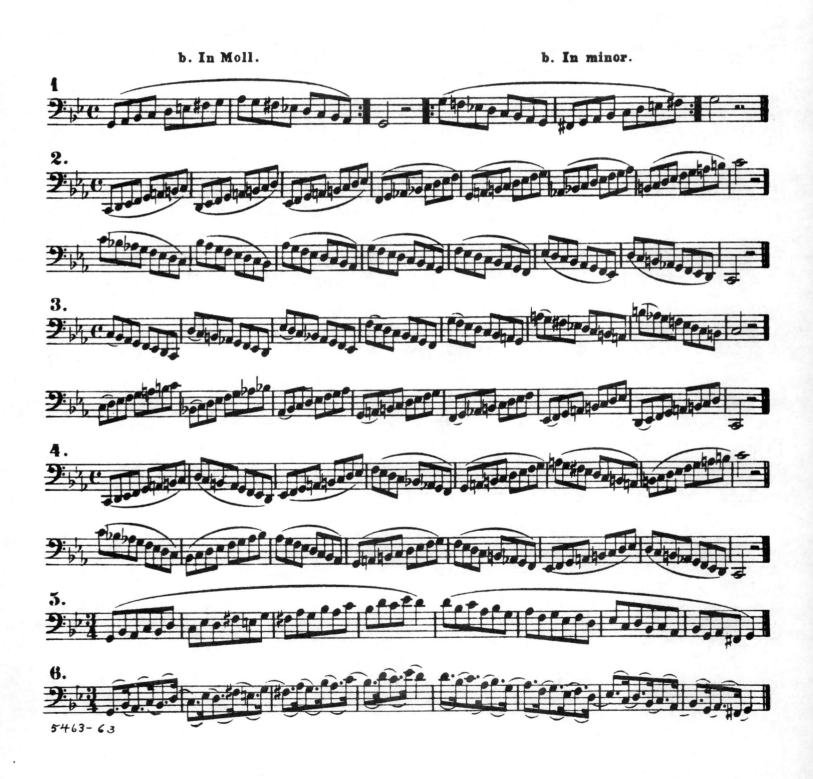

Chromatic Scales

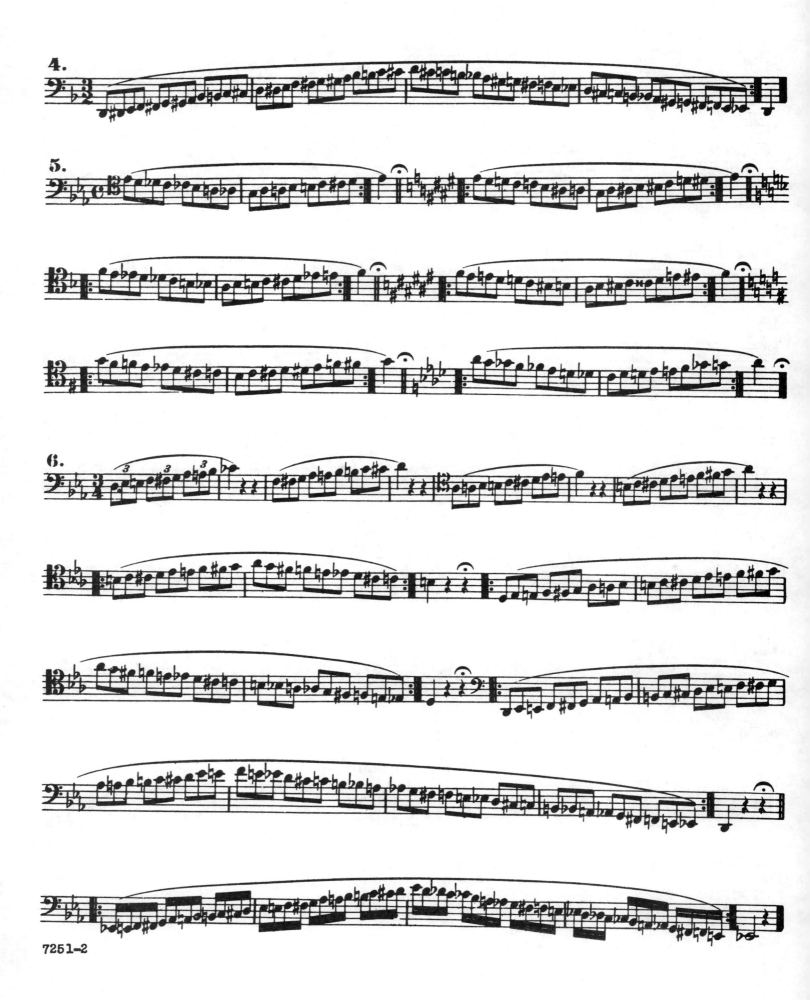

Akkorde.   Chords.

Der Dreiklang. — *The triad.*

Auf dieselbe Weise wie hier der Cdur-Akkord sind auch alle andern Dur - und Moll - Dreiklänge auszuführen.

All the major and minor triads are to be practiced in the same manner as indicated here in the C-major chord.

Der Dominantseptimenakkord. — *The dominant chord of the seventh.*

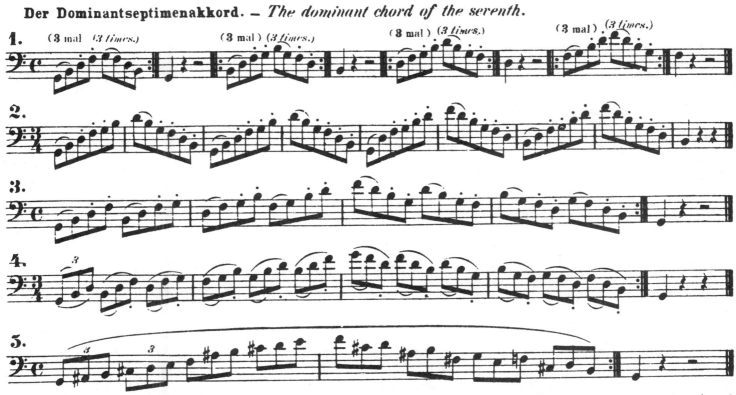

Auf gleiche Weise sind die übrigen Dominantseptimen-akkorde zu behandeln.

The other dominant chords of the seventh to be played in like manner.

72

c. Der verminderte Septimenakkord. — *The diminished chord of the 7th.*

Ebenso wie dieser sind auch die beiden andern verminderten Septimenakkorde: und durchzunehmen. Bekanntlich giebt es nur drei, dem Klange nach verschiedene verminderte Septimenakkorde.

The other two, diminished chords of the 7th in the same way: und. It is well known that there are only three, different-sounding chords of the 7th.

d. Verschiedene Nebenseptimenakkorde. — *Various secondary chords of the 7th.*

riten.- - - - - -

5463- 63

SCALE EXERCISES

IN ALL KEYS

C. ALMENRAEDER
Revised by P.X. Laube

C MAJOR

7253-16

74

A MINOR (Melodic)

G MAJOR

E MINOR

D MAJOR

B MINOR

A MAJOR

F SHARP MINOR

E MAJOR

C SHARP MINOR

B MAJOR

G SHARP MINOR

F MAJOR

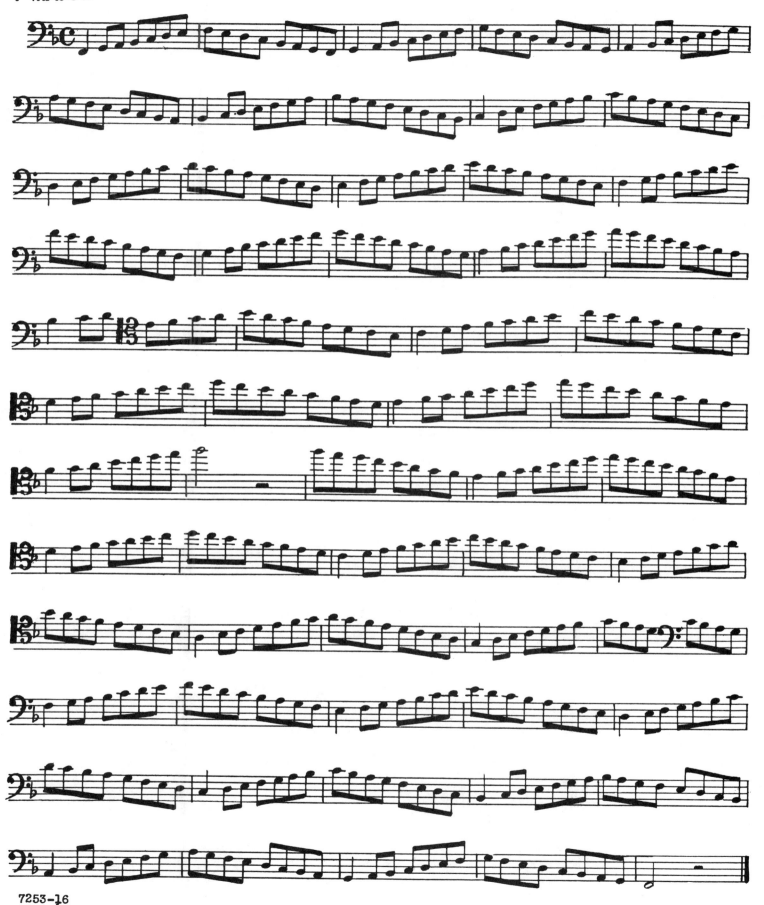

D MINOR

Bb MAJOR

G MINOR

84

Eb MAJOR

7253-16

C MINOR

Ab MAJOR

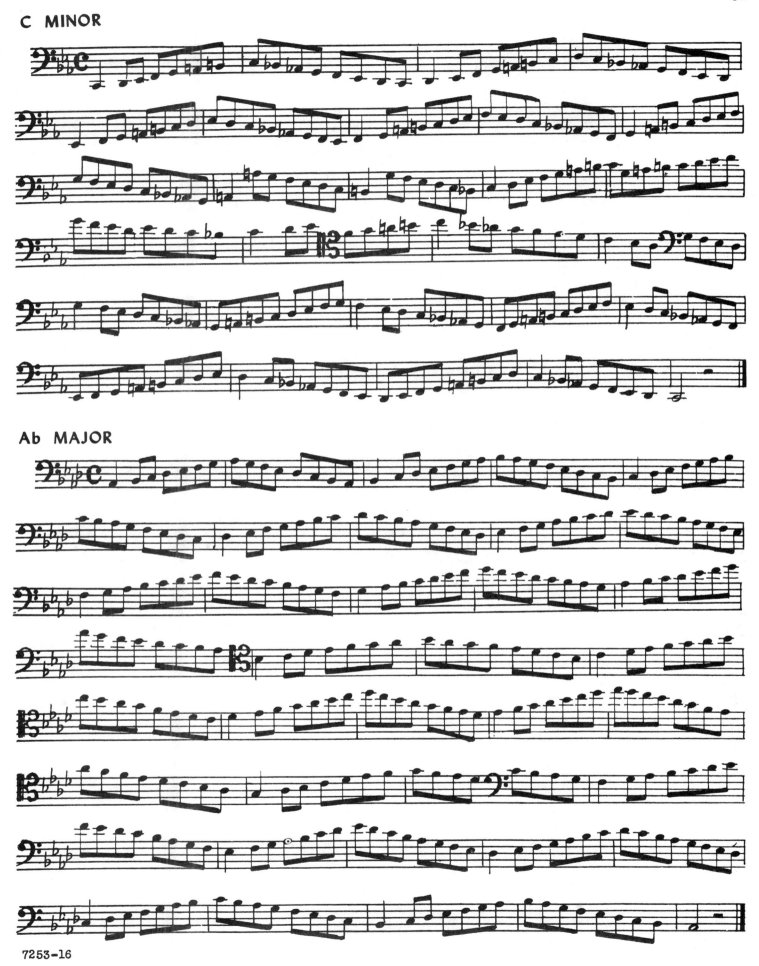

7253-16

86

MINOR

Db MAJOR

7253-16

Bb MINOR

88

Gb MAJOR

Eb MINOR

STUDIES

In all Keys.

№ 1.

BASSOON

L. Milde, Op. 24.

5474-16

The Cundy: Bettoney Co., Boston, Mass.

№ 2.

5474-26

№ 3.

№ 4.

5474-26

№ 5.

№ 6.

№ 7.

№ 8.

№ 9.

№ 10.

№ 11.

5474-26

№ 12.

5474-26

№ 13.

№ 14.

5474-16

№ 15.

5474-26

№ 16.

№ 17.

№ 18.

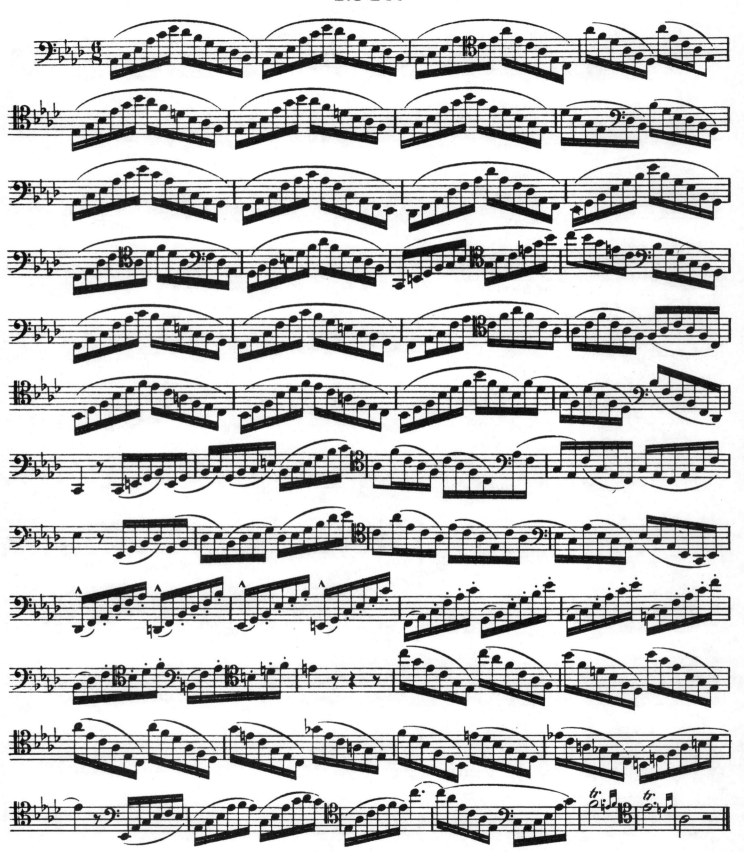

№ 19.

№ 20.

Nº 21.

№ 22.

№ 23.

№ 24.

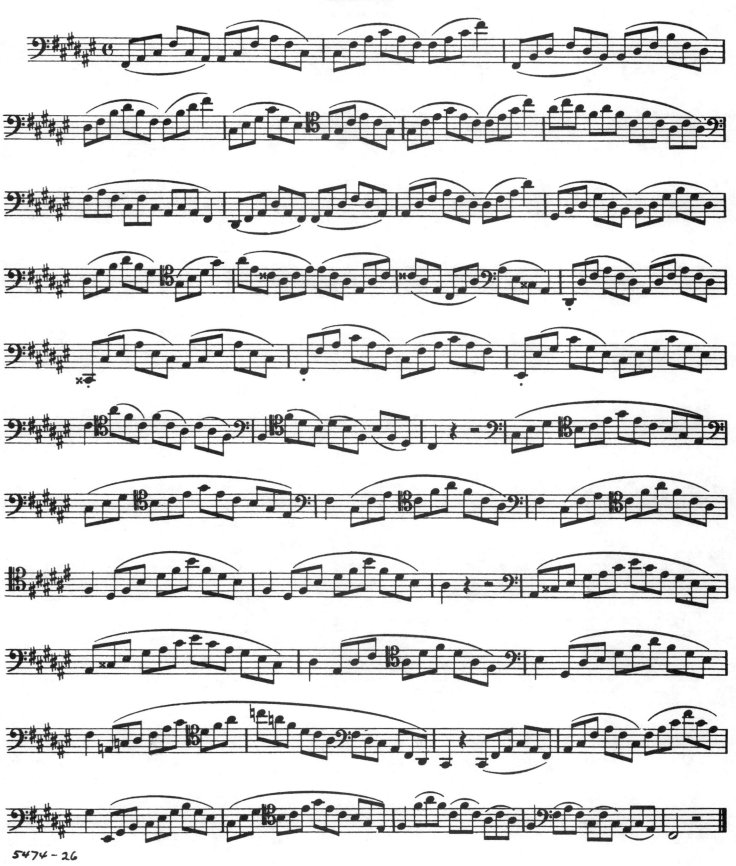

5474-26

№ 25.

Fifty Bassoon Studies

Julius Weissenborn, Op. 8. Vol. II.

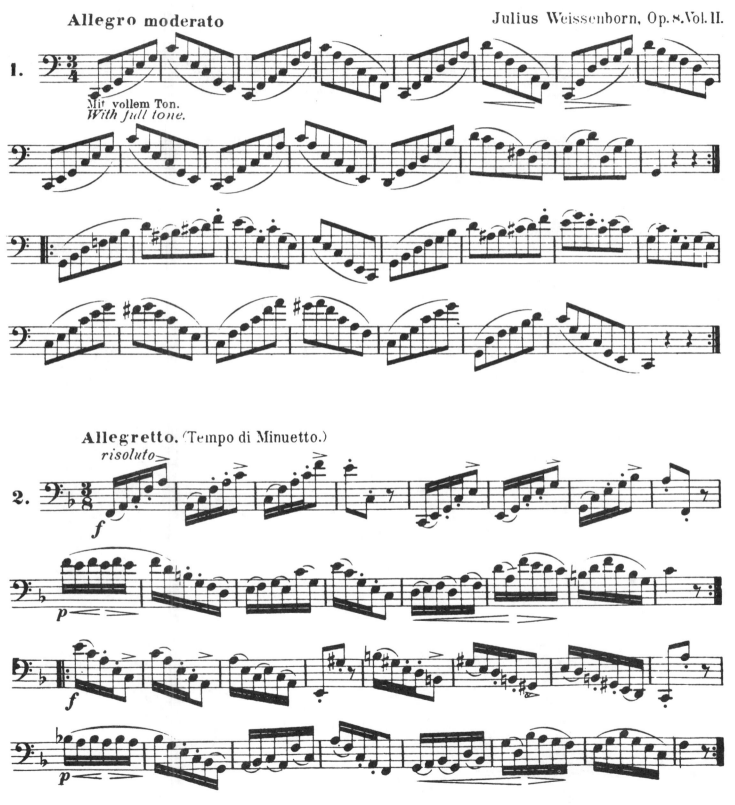

Allegretto grazioso.

6.

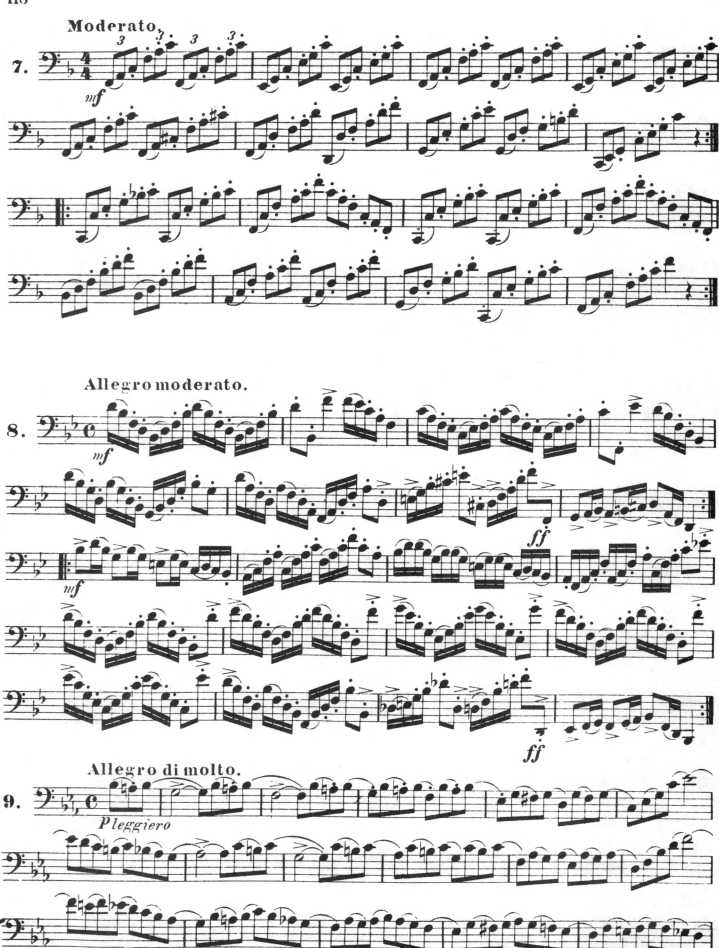

7215-41

Vivace.

11.

mf

Lebhaft. *Lively.*

Siehe B-dur-Sinfonie von Rob. Schumann
See: Sinphonie B♭ major by Rob. Schumann

Allegro.

12.

p

cresc.   *f*   *p*

rfp   *rfp*   *rfp*

marcato

f   *p*   *cresc.*

f

124

Allegro.

16.

7215-41

Allegro ma non troppo.

17.

Allegro moderato.

18.

130

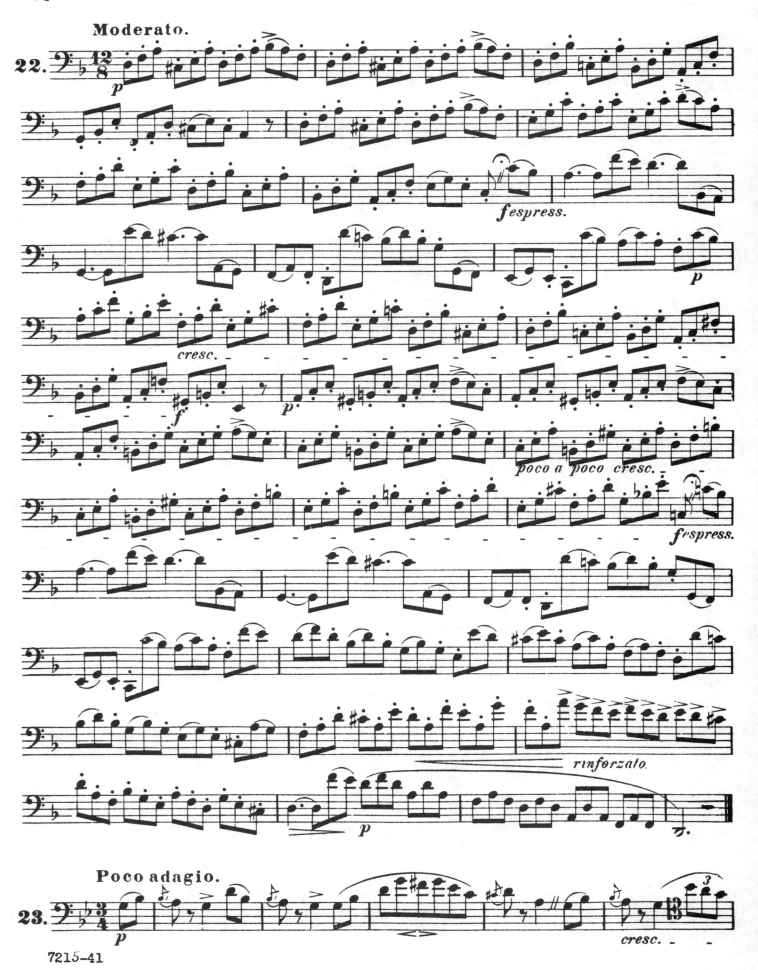

7215-41

Ausführ:
Exec:

P delicato

rf

Da capo al fine.

Allegro con brio.

24.

mf

Da capo sin' al fine.

Vivace.

27.

un poco riten.

Scherzo.
Allegro vivace.

28.

Trio.

Fine.

p dolce

Da capo sin' al fine.

Allegro con fuoco.

29.

cresc. — — — f

Allegro assai.

30.

Andante, quasi allegretto.

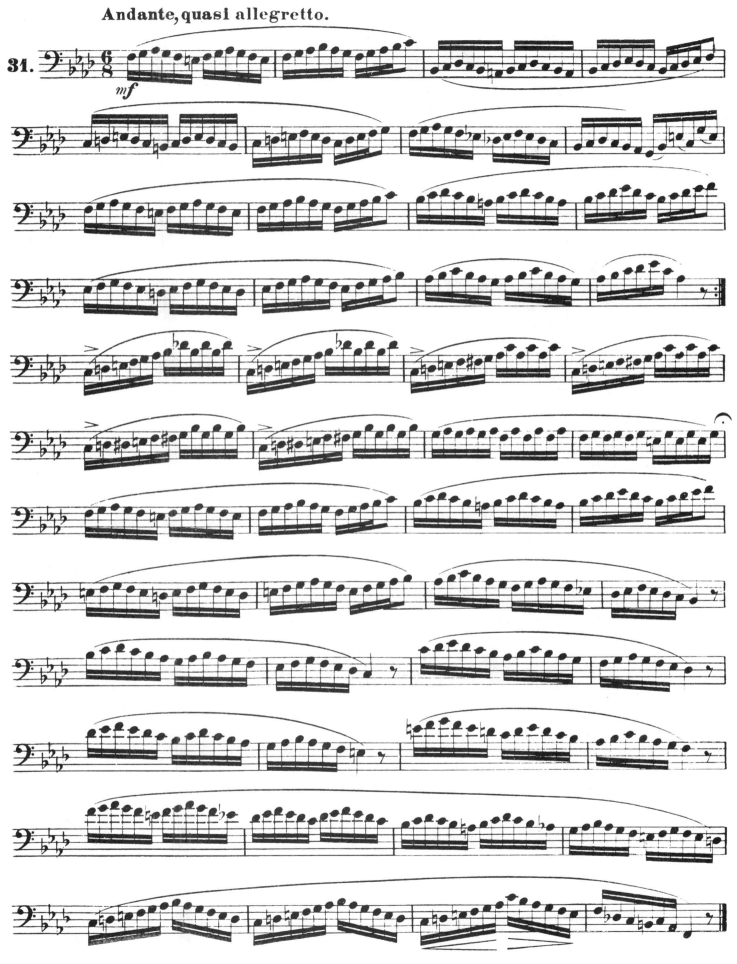

Tempo di marcia.

32.

Andantino.

33.

Andante con moto, quasi allegro moderato.

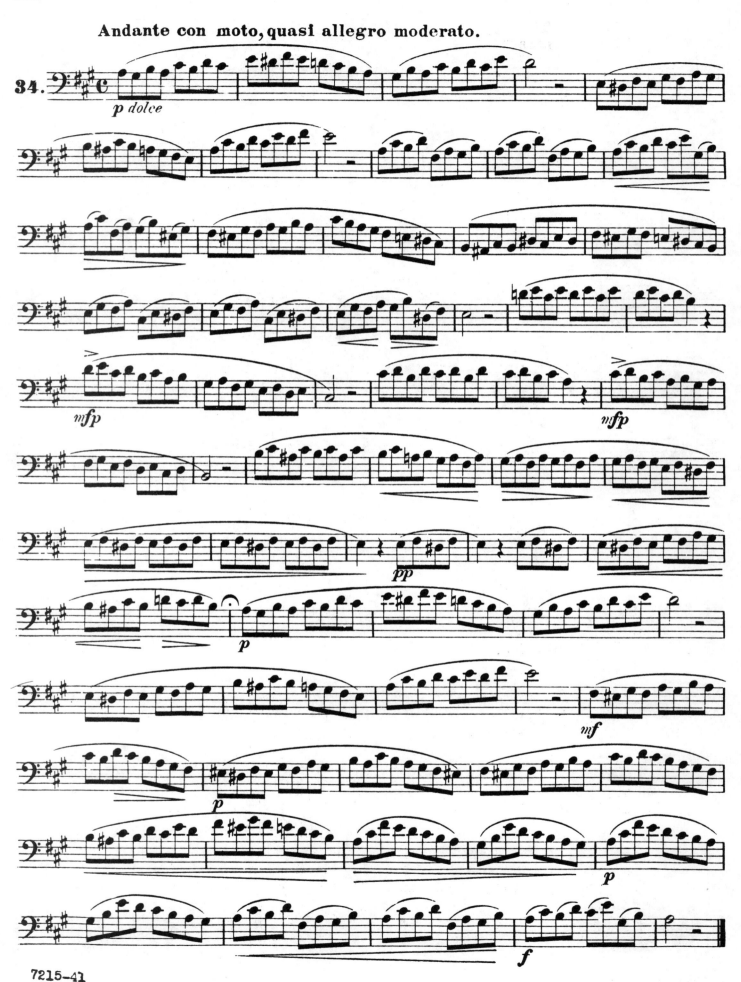

Andante maestoso.

35.

Allegro moderato.

36.

Allegro con fuoco.

Allegro ma non troppo.
(Alla breve.)

42.

148

Adagio, ma non strasciando.

43.

Tema con variazioni.
Andante. Intrada.

44.

dimin. _ _ _ _ _ *ritard.* _ _ _

Tema.
a tempo

poco f *Mit Naivetät.*
With naivete.

Var. I.

p

sempre stacc.

Var. II.

mf

|1.|2.|

Var. III.

f

(Das 2. Mal piano.)

|1.|2.|

p

f

p

f

Var. IV.

Coda.

Larghetto.

45.

Andante con moto, quasi allegretto.

Andante con moto.

Andante con moto.

48.

154

Andante sostenuto.

49.

ritard.

Ungarische Fantasie
Andante e Rondo Ongarese.

Solo Bassoon

C. M. v. Weber, Op. **35**.

The Cundy-Bettoney Co., Boston, Mass.

Solo Bassoon

7252-4

Musical Terms.

TERM.	MEANING.	ABBREVIATION.	TERM.	MEANING.	ABBREVIATION.
Accelerando	With gradually increasing velocity of movement.	Accel.	Obligato	Indispensable.	
Adagio	Very slow.	Ad<u>o</u>.	Piacere	Will, pleasure.	
Ad libitum	At will, pleasure or discretion.	Ad lib.	Piano	Soft.	*p*.
Affetuoso	Tender and affecting.	Afto.	Pianissimo	Very soft.	*pp*.
Agitato	With agitation, anxiously.	Agt<u>o</u>.	Piu	More.	
Allegro	Quick, lively.	All<u>o</u>.	Poco	A little.	
Allegretto	Not so quick as Allegro.	Alltto.	Poco a poco	By degrees, gradually.	
Andante	A slow movement.	And<u>te</u>.	Presto	Quick.	
Andantino	Somewhat slower than Andante.	And<u>no</u>.	Prestissimo	Very quick.	
Animato	With animation and spirit.		Primo	First.	
Appoggiato	Dwelt or leaned upon.	App<u>o</u>.	Quasi	In the style of.	
Aria	An air or song.		Rallentando	Slower and softer by degrees.	rall.
Ariosa	In the style of a song.		Ritenuto	Gradually slower.	rit.
Assai	Very, extremely.		Recitative	Musical declamation.	
A tempo	In the original time.	A tem.	Rinforzando	Suddenly increasing in power.	
A tempo guisto	In strict and exact time.		Segno	Sign.	
Ben	Well.		Sempre	Always, throughout.	
Bis	To be played twice.		Semplice	Simple.	
Brio or Brillante	Gay, brilliant, sparkling.		Smorzando	Dying away by degrees.	Smorz.
Cadenza	An extemporaneous embelishment.		Spirito	With spirit, lively.	
Cadence	Closing strain.		Sostenuto	Sustained.	Sost<u>o</u>.
Calando	Softer and slower.		Solo	For single instrument or voice.	
Cantabile	Graceful, pleasing.		Staccato	Short, detached, distinct.	
Capo	Head or beginning.		Subito	Quickly.	
Coda	A second or added ending.	C.	Stringendo	Accelerating the degree of movement.	
Con	With.		Sotto	Subdued.	
Comado	Easily, unrestrainedly.		Tacet	Silent.	
Crescendo	Gradually increasing the sound.	Cres.	Tardo	Slow.	
Da	By, for, from.	D.	Tempo	Time.	
Da Capo	From the beginning.	D.C.	Troppo	Too much.	
Delicato	Delicately.		Tutti	all.	
Diminuendo	Gradually diminishing the sound.	Dim.	Tenuto	Sustained full notes.	
Dal Segno	From the sign.	D.S.	Thema or Tema	Subject or Theme.	
Declamando	In the style of declamation.		Vivace	Quick.	
Decrescendo	Gradually decreasing the sound.		Vivo	Lively.	
Dolce	Soft, sweet, delicate.	Dol.	Volto subito	Turn page quickly.	V s.
Dolante or Doloroso	Mournful, pathetic.				
Duet	For two instruments or voices.				
Elegante	With elegance.				
Energico	With enegy.				
Espressivo	With expression.	Express.			
Fine, Fin or Finale	The end of movement.	Fine.			
Forte	Loud.	*f*.			
Fortissimo	Very Loud.	*ff*.			
Ferzando	Sudden increase of power.	*fz*.			
Fuoco	Fire, animation.				
Furioso	With fire.				
Grandioso	Grand style.	Grand<u>o</u>.			
Grave	Very slow, solemnly.				
Grazioso	Smoothly, gracefully.				
Guisto	In strict time.				
Gusto	Elegantly.				
Glisando	To slide.				
Gruppetto	A group of notes, a turn.				
Impetuoso	Impetuously.				
Irresoluto	Irresolutely.				
Largo	Slow.				
Larghissimo	Extremely slow.				
Larghetto	Slow, but not slow as Largo.				
Legato	Smooth, connected.				
Lento	In slow time.				
Lentando	Gradually slower and softer.				
Maestoso	Majestically.	Maest<u>o</u>.			
Marcato	In strong marked style.				
Marziale	Martial.	Marzl<u>e</u>.			
Meno	Less.	Men.			
Moderato	In moderate time.	Mod<u>to</u>.			
Molto	Much or very.				
Morendo	Gradually dying away.				
Mosso	Motion.				
Mato	Agitation.				
Non	Not.				

TERMS WITH ADDITION OF OTHER WORDS.

TERM.	MEANING.
Andante ma non troppo	Slow, but not too slow.
Andante cantabile	Slow, but in singing style.
Andante con molto	Very slow.
Andante maestoso	Slow, majestic.
Andantino sostenuto	Slow and sustained.
Allegro agitato	Quick, with agitation.
Allegro assai	Very quick.
Allegro con brio	Quick with brilliancy.
Allegro con fuoco	Quick, with fire.
Allegro con spirito	Quick, with spirit.
Allegro moderato	Moderately quick.
Allegro piu mosso	Rather quick.
Allegro vivace	Very quick.
Ben marcato	Well marked.
Con forza	With force.
Con brio	With brilliancy.
Con brio ed animato	With brilliancy and animation.
Con espressivo	With expression.
Con dolecessa	With delicacy.
Con dolore	Mournfully.
Con energico	With energy.
Con fuoco	With ardor or fire.
Con grazio	With grace and elegance.
Con gusto	With exactness and taste.
Con moto	With emotion.
Con spirito	With spirit, animation.
Dolce con gusto	Sweetly with elegance.
Meno mosso	Less quickly.
Meno vivo	Less spirit.
Piu lento	Rather slow.
Più presto	Rather accelerated.